Yun's Visit

William Chin
Illustrated by Doreen Gay-Kassel

It was Saturday afternoon, and Yun and her mother were walking to Cathy's home. Cathy had just moved into Yun's neighborhood, and they had become friends at school. Yun was happy to have a new friend, but she was nervous about going to her house.

"Mother," said Yun, "I wonder if Cathy's family is different from our family. What if we don't like or do the same things?"

"Every family is different, but I'm sure everything will be fine," said Yun's mother.

"I really like Cathy, so I'm sure I'll like her family, too," said Yun.

Yun and her mother went to the front door, and Yun rang the doorbell.

"Come in," said Cathy with a smile, as she opened the door. "This is my mother."

"Thank you for inviting Yun to play in your home today," said Yun's mother. She handed Cathy's mother a box of candy to thank her for inviting Yun to visit.

"Thank you for this candy!" said Cathy's mother. "Welcome to our home, Yun."

Yun said good-bye to her mother and followed Cathy into her home.

After Cathy showed Yun her bedroom, the girls went outside to play soccer. Cathy showed Yun how to stop the ball with her feet, and Yun taught Cathy how to hit the ball with her head. Yun was glad that they both liked soccer.

Soon Cathy's mother came outside and said, "Girls, would you like some of the lemonade I just made?"

Yun and Cathy were thirsty, so they followed her inside.

Cathy's mother gave each of the girls a glass of lemonade, and the girls talked and laughed while they drank it. They were having so much fun that Cathy asked her mother if Yun could sleep over. Then the girls thought of all of the things that they could do together.

“We could bake cookies!” said Yun.

“We could play games on the computer and then write a story!” said Cathy.

Suddenly Yun got worried.

"I've never slept at a friend's home before. I don't know if my parents will allow it," Yun told Cathy. "I have to call my mother so that I can ask her."

"I've had other friends sleep over. I hope she lets you stay," said Cathy.

Yun called her mother.

"Mother," said Yun, "Cathy wants to know if I could sleep over at her home tonight."

"Why? You have your own bed," said Yun's mother, "so I think you should sleep at home."

"OK," said Yun with a big sigh, "I'll tell Cathy."

“My mother said that I should sleep at home,” Yun told Cathy.

“Oh no,” said Cathy, “we were going to have so much fun!”

“I know,” said Yun sadly. “I wish I could stay, too.”

“I have an idea!” said Cathy. “If you can’t sleep over, maybe you could eat dinner here. We’re having pizza.”

Yun called her mother again. "I know that I can't sleep over at Cathy's house," said Yun, "but may I eat dinner here?"

"Why do you want to eat dinner there? We have food for you here," said Yun's mother.

"They're having pizza," said Yun, "and you know how much I *love* pizza!"

"Well, I guess it's OK," said Yun's mother. "Have a good time!"

After they ate dinner, Yun's mother came to take Yun home.

"Thank you for dinner," Yun said to Cathy's mother.

"You're welcome," she said. "I'm so glad that Cathy found such a good friend at her new school."

"Next time, Cathy can come and eat dinner with our family," said Yun's mother, smiling.

"That sounds like fun!" said Cathy.